A NEW DIRECTION

A Cognitive-Behavioral Treatment Curriculum

SHORT-TERM WORKBOOK

Release & Reintegration Preparation

*Mapping a Life
of Recovery & Freedom
for Chemically Dependent
Criminal Offenders*

**A Collaboration of Chemical Dependency Professionals from
the Minnesota Department of Corrections and the Hazelden Foundation**

HAZELDEN

Hazelden
Center City, Minnesota 55012-0176

1-800-328-9000
1-651-213-4590 (Fax)
www.hazelden.org

©2002 by Hazelden Foundation
All rights reserved. Published 2002
Printed in the United States of America

ISBN 13: 978-1-56838-863-2

Cover design by David Spohn
Interior design by Terri Kinne
Illustrations by Patrice Barton

Hazelden Foundation, a national nonprofit organization founded in 1949, helps people reclaim their lives from the disease of addiction. Built on decades of knowledge and experience, Hazelden's comprehensive approach to addiction addresses the full range of individual, family, and professional needs, including addiction treatment and continuing care services for youth and adults, publishing, research, higher learning, public education, and advocacy.

A life of recovery is lived "one day at a time." Hazelden publications, both educational and inspirational, support and strengthen lifelong recovery. In 1954, Hazelden published *Twenty-Four Hours a Day,* the first daily meditation book for recovering alcoholics, and Hazelden continues to publish works to inspire and guide individuals in treatment and recovery, and their loved ones. Professionals who work to prevent and treat addiction also turn to Hazelden for evidence-based curricula, informational materials, and videos for use in schools, treatment programs, and correctional programs.

Through published works, Hazelden extends the reach of hope, encouragement, help, and support to individuals, families, and communities affected by addiction and related issues.

For questions about Hazelden publications,
please call **800-328-9000** or visit us online at **hazelden.org/bookstore.**

CONTENTS

A NEW DIRECTION

A Cognitive-Behavioral Treatment Curriculum

Acknowledgments

Thanks to all who have contributed to this curriculum:

Sheryl Ramstad Hvass
Commissioner, Minnesota Department of Corrections

Peter Bell
Executive Vice President, Hazelden Publishing and Educational Services

James D. Kaul, Ph.D.
Director, TRIAD Chemical Dependency Program
Minnesota Department of Corrections

Will Alexander
Sex Offender/Chemical Dependency Services Unit, Minnesota Department of Corrections

Minnesota Department of Corrections

Sex Offender Treatment Program at Lino Lakes Minnesota Correctional Facility

Robin Goldman, Director
Jim Berg, Program Supervisor
Brian Heinsohn, Corrections Program Therapist
Greg Kraft, Corrections Program Therapist
K. Kaprice Borowski Krebsbach, Corrections Program Therapist
Kevin Nelson, Corrections Program Therapist
Tim Schrupp, Corrections Program Therapist
Pamela Stanchfield, Corrections Program Therapist
Jason Terwey, Corrections Program Therapist
John Vieno, Corrections Program Therapist
Cynthia Woodward, Corrections Program Therapist

TRIAD Chemical Dependency Program at Lino Lakes Minnesota Correctional Facility

Launie Zaffke, Supervisor
Randy Tenge, Supervisor
Carmen Ihlenfeldt, Acting Supervisor
Thomas A. Berner, Corrections Program Therapist
Toni Brezina, Corrections Program Therapist
Jeanie Cooke, Corrections Program Therapist
Ronald J. DeGidio, Corrections Program Therapist
Susan DeGidio, Corrections Program Therapist
Maryann Edgerley, Corrections Program Therapist
Connie Garritsen, Corrections Program Therapist
Gerald Gibcke, Corrections Program Therapist
Anthony Hoheisel, Corrections Program Therapist
Deidra Jones, Corrections Program Therapist
Beth Matchey, Corrections Program Therapist
Jack McGee, Corrections Program Therapist
Jackie Michaelson, Corrections Program Therapist

Hal Palmer, Corrections Program Therapist
Terrance Peach, Corrections Program Therapist
Holly Petersen, Corrections Program Therapist
Linda Rose, Corrections Program Therapist
Kathy Thompson, Corrections Program Therapist
Beverly Welo, Corrections Program Therapist

Reshape Chemical Dependency Program at Saint Cloud Minnesota Correctional Facility

Robert L. Jungbauer, Director
Christine Fortson, Corrections Program Therapist
Tracanne Nelson, Corrections Program Therapist
Jeffrey D. Spies, Corrections Program Therapist

Atlantis Chemical Dependency Program at Stillwater Minnesota Correctional Facility

Bob Reed, Director
Dennis Abitz, Corrections Program Therapist
Bill Burgin, Corrections Program Therapist
Tom Shipp, Corrections Program Therapist

New Dimensions Chemical Dependency Program at Faribault Minnesota Correctional Facility

Michael Coleman, Supervisor
Michele Caron, Corrections Program Therapist

Central Office

Jim Linehan, Corrections Program Therapist

Minnesota Department of Corrections Supervising Agents

Russ Stricker, Correctional Unit Supervisor
Bobbi Chevaliar-Jones, Intensive Supervised Release Agent
William Hafner, Corrections Agent
Gregory Fletcher, 180 Degrees Halfway House

In Addition:

Writers: Corrine Casanova, Deborah Johnson, Stephen Lehman, Joseph M. Moriarity, Paul Schersten. **Designer:** Terri Kinne. **Typesetters:** Terri Kinne, Julie Szamocki. **Illustrator:** Patrice Barton. **Prepress:** Don Freeman, Kathryn Kjorlien, Rachelle Kuehl, Joan Seim, Tracy Snyder, David Spohn. **Editor:** Corrine Casanova. **Copy editors:** Monica Dwyer Abress, Kristal Leebrick, Caryn Pernu. **Proofreaders:** Catherine Broberg, Kristal Leebrick. **Marketer:** Michelle Samlaska. **Video production manager:** Alexis Scott.

Special thanks: Any Color Painting Company; Blue Moon Production Company; Eden Re-entry Services; inmates and staff of Lino Lakes, Rush City, and Stillwater Minnesota Correctional Facilities.

Special thanks to Hazelden: Nancy Alliegro, Derrick Crim, Joe Fittipaldi, Carole Kilpela, Nick Motu, Karin Nord, Patricia Owen, Rebecca Post, Teri Ryan, Ann Standing, Sue Thill, and Kris VanHoof-Haines.

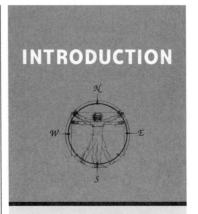

Starting Over

Your release date is almost here. Your life is about to change. Starting over can be a positive experience. When you step out into the real world again, you'll find that much has changed since you became incarcerated. *You* are a different person, too.

You're living in a highly structured world right now. Rules guide every hour of your day. People make sure you follow those rules. That's about to change. The more time you spend on the outside, the less supervision you will have. You will be responsible for your own thoughts, behaviors, and actions. That will probably be one of the biggest challenges for you.

After all, you will be trying to *change the way you've always lived,* in big ways.

Staying Sober and Avoiding Criminal Behavior Are Your Main Goals

Like all addicts, you'll be faced each morning with doubts—that you won't be able to stay sober or avoid committing crimes. *Staying sober and avoiding criminal behavior must be your top priorities.* Whenever you make a decision, even a small one, consider those two goals. You must learn to be personally responsible. Know your obligations to yourself and others, and live up to them.

This workbook will help you make decisions about some basic aspects of your new life:

- where you will live
- where you will work
- how you will spend your spare time
- who you will use for support

This workbook will help you set specific, realistic goals and plans for your new life in recovery.

Stress and Frustration

You *will* experience stress. The outside world is not set up to make life easy for the ex-offender. *Feeling stress will not mean you are doing something wrong.* Everybody feels stress. That's because the world isn't set up to make life easy for anybody. Stress is normal. What's important is how you react to that stress and handle your emotions.

You can't control the actions of others. You can't control all events in your life. But you *can* manage your own reactions, both mental and emotional, and you *can control your actions.* You can *choose* to act in ways that do not lead to chemical use or criminal activity. You can make choices that *will not* put you back behind bars.

This workbook will help you make a plan for the first few days and weeks after your release. By doing this, your chances of never returning to life behind bars will improve greatly. You will also make long-term plans for your new life.

The First Few Days Following Release

Any ex-offender will tell you that the first few days after release can be really hard, especially if you don't have plans for the basics, such as where you're going to sleep or how you're going to eat or make money. "Oh man, I just found myself wanting to *make up time,*" said one offender who failed quickly in his new life.

Flexibility

Flexibility in how you think and act is the key to successful reintegration. Rigid, angry, irrational reactions to stress got you behind bars. In your new life, when faced with a stressful situation, you must *consider the options.* You have options, or choices, in how you think and in how you react. You can be flexible.

"Man, it's a big change. It's not just going to work automatically. It's up to you. You're the same person in a lot of ways, of course, but then you have to be a totally different guy than you used to be, too."

— Ron H.,
former offender,
Connecticut

Setting Goals and Planning

Success comes when you set goals and then make plans for meeting those goals. Goal setting helps you to be proactive in dealing with life, rather than just reactive, as you used to be. We'll teach you *how to set* realistic goals.

For some ex-offenders, setting goals can seem stupid, a waste of time, or both. After all, you might feel that your life won't get any better and that you "never get any breaks." ***Victim-stance*** thinking is easy to fall into. But you've got to avoid that old way of thinking.

It's important to be flexible when you set your goals and in the steps you take to reach them. Being flexible is a skill. That's what a healthy, responsible life is all about.

Self-Awareness and How Others See You

Many ex-offenders think that everybody knows their past and judges them. That's not true. Many people will have no idea that you've been incarcerated. However, people *will* react to your criminal record once they learn you have one. These could be people you know already or a possible land-lord or employer. They may make a comment that hooks your shame and guilt, such as telling you they won't hire or rent to you. On the other hand, others might view you as a role model because you've been incarcerated. Still others might be frightened of you and avoid you.

Always focus on the fact that you are in control of your behavior and emotions. You need to show others through your actions that you have changed. Remember, *you can't control others' perceptions or actions, but you can mange your own thinking and your own emotions, and you can control your own response in any situation.*

Be a Role Model

As you head out into your new life, realize that you are *an important person to a lot of people.* This includes the friends you've made both inside and outside this program, other ex-offenders, and family members who live responsibly and want you to do the same. They all want you to make it.

Be Realistic, But Don't Sell Yourself Short

Throughout this workbook, we will emphasize two messages:

1. Goals should be *specific and attainable.* Don't set your goals too high. Otherwise, you will become frustrated and set yourself up for failure.

2. Be *ambitious.* It's time to develop new skills and interests. Learn from your past experiences. Always aim to improve yourself and your situation.

If you play things straight, you can find success in your new life. Set goals. Make plans. Live your daily life with honesty and responsibility. Always be on the lookout for the little patterns and decisions that could lead you back to your old using and criminal behaviors. By just being aware, you will start to experience the benefits of living a crime-free, drug-free life. It's now time to start planning the rest of your life. This isn't a job for just anyone—only you can do it.

■

Set goals. Make plans. Live your daily life with honesty and responsibility.

As you head out into your new life, realize that you are an important person to a lot of people.

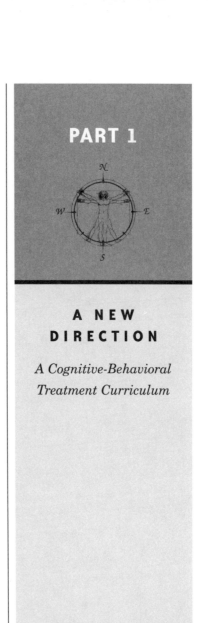

PART 1

Criminal and Addictive Thinking

It's time to set some goals and make plans for your life on the outside. Before you do this, however, you'll want to think about how your plans and goals for the future relate to your own criminal and addictive thinking patterns.

Criminal thinking patterns are common to all criminals. They are the thinking that says it is all right for you to violate others or the property of others. **Addictive thinking patterns** are common to all addicts, though not every addict has every single one. Addictive thinking patterns say that continuing to use alcohol and other drugs is okay no matter what the consequences are to yourself or others. Addictive thinking patterns overlap greatly with criminal thinking patterns. The two reinforce and drive each other.

Your Own Criminal and Addictive Issues

This section reviews some material from the *Criminal & Addictive Thinking* module and the *Drug & Alcohol Education* module. If you haven't worked through those workbooks yet, the concept of criminal and addictive thinking patterns will be new to you, and this section will be especially valuable for you. You'll be "thinking about your thinking," possibly for the first time ever.

We'll review criminal and addictive thinking patterns. Then we'll ask you

- What have you learned about yourself?
- What are your issues?

Thinking: The Basics

Your thinking is like a map—a map your mind uses to get around. When you're somewhere new, not just any old map will do; you need a good map. You need a map that fits the world you're in. And you need a map that tells you what you need to know.

Our mental map tells us about what's going on. Without it, we're lost. But our map can also mislead us. Maps become old. As our lives change and we grow older, our map needs to change, too. If it doesn't change, it becomes faulty. When this happens, we interpret situations in ways that lead to trouble. Your faulty map explains why you are reading this while incarcerated. Your map didn't work for you—it led you to where you are right now.

Constructing a New Thought Map

The good news is, you're in charge of your mental map. You can figure out which parts of your old, faulty mental map don't work. You can learn how to begin the process of erasing those parts and start creating a new, effective map. Will it take effort? Yes. Can you do it? Yes, you can—if you make that decision.

Because of your faulty map, you use

- **rigid thinking**—thinking that tells you that you know exactly what's going on, even when you don't

- **automatic thinking**—thinking that happens all the time in response to certain situations, and which usually gets you in trouble

"Man, I would get myself screwed up from the get-go. Anything could happen. I'd think it was against me or something I needed to get mad about. I saw it as proof that I should just take what I wanted anyway. I was a real jerk sometimes."

— Will S.,
former offender,
Illinois

Criminal and Addictive Thinking Patterns

As noted earlier, criminal and addictive thinking patterns are linked. Each criminal thinking pattern is closely related to an addictive thinking pattern. They are defined below.

Criminal Thinking Patterns	Addictive Thinking Patterns
• victim stance	• self-pity stance
• "good person" stance	• "good person" stance
• "unique person" stance	• "unique person" stance
• fear of exposure	• fear of exposure
• lack-of-time perspective	• lack-of-time perspective
• selective effort	• selective effort
• use of power to control	• use of deceit to control
• seek excitement first	• seek pleasure first
• ownership stance	• ownership stance

Now we'll take a closer look at those patterns.

1. **Victim stance.** This *criminal* thinking pattern allows you to blame others for situations you usually created for yourself. You make excuses and point your finger at others, claiming you were the one who was really wronged. You try to justify your behavior. **Self-pity stance.** This *addictive* thinking pattern makes you think the world is just out to get you. You claim that your life is so miserable and screwed up, why shouldn't you drink or use drugs?

2. **"Good person" stance.** When you adopt this *criminal* thinking pattern, you consider yourself to be a good person, no matter what. You work hard to present that image to others. In fact, you may not only consider yourself a good person, but may think you're better than others! As a

"good person" stance addictive thinker, you focus on the good things you've done and ignore the harm.

3. **"Unique person" stance.** This *criminal* thinking pattern allows you to think no one in the whole world is like you or has experienced what you have. Rules don't apply to you. You commit crimes because you never think you'll get caught. You believe that if you think it, then it must be that way. You also use *"unique person" stance* to feed your addiction. Maybe you think your alcohol or other drug use makes you especially cool.

4. **Fear of exposure.** You act like you are fearless, yet you're full of fear. You fear that you're nobody and that you'll be found out; you're afraid that you'll be exposed as being full of fear. One of your biggest fears is the fear of fear! *Fear of exposure* addictive thinking is fear of self-knowledge, excessive or inappropriate trust, addict pride, and zero state. Zero state is a fear that you cannot change.

5. **Lack-of-time perspective.** When you use this *criminal* thinking pattern, you do not learn from past experiences or plan for the future. You see behaviors as isolated events. Your philosophy is "I want it, and I want it *now*." You expect to be a big success with little or no effort. You make choices based on what you *want* to be true, rather than what *is* true. When you adopt this *addictive* thinking pattern, getting high is the most important thing in your life; you live only in the present when you are high and only in the near future ("How can I get more soon?") when you are not high. *Lack-of-time perspective* addictive thinking helps you do that.

The zero state consists of these beliefs:
- You are nothing.
- Everyone else also believes you are worthless.
- Your "worthlessness" will last forever and can never be changed.

As a criminal thinker, you don't put any effort into achieving responsible goals.

6. **Selective effort.** As a criminal thinker, you don't put any effort into achieving responsible goals. You go for the quick fix, the easy bucks—the scam. As an addictive thinker, you will go to great trouble to get and use alcohol or other drugs, but you can't be bothered by daily obligations of responsible living. That's *selective effort.*

7. **Use of power to control.** This thinking pattern is motivated by selfishness. You do it because controlling others makes *you* feel good. When victim-stance thinking doesn't work for you, you use power to control. If you can't manipulate others by gaining their sympathy, you try to do it through fear and intimidation. **Use of deceit to control** addictive thinking says it is okay to use chemicals and to lie about it. When people challenge you on this, you want to control them through your deceit.

8. **Seek excitement first.** These thoughts keep you away from responsible behavior. You use this pattern of criminal thinking because you don't like to be bored, you don't like to be alone much, you live only for the day, and you don't consider the consequences of your behavior. As an addictive thinker, you **seek pleasure first.** This is the pleasure of getting high. You seek this pleasure without considering the serious physical, mental, and legal consequences.

9. **Ownership stance.** This criminal thinking pattern has one-way boundaries. It allows you to say, "What's mine is mine, and what's yours is mine." It also gives you the idea that people are property. You might say, "She's mine, so she has to do as I say." With *ownership stance* addictive thinking, this disregard for the property rights of others comes from your obsession with getting high. You do whatever it takes to feed your addiction.

Your Criminal and Addictive Thinking Patterns

➤ List the three criminal thinking patterns and the closely related addictive thinking patterns that you can most relate to.

1. _____

2. _____

3. _____

➤ In group, explain why you use these thinking patterns the most. What have you learned about yourself by listening to your peers talk about their patterns?

_____

_____

_____

_____

➤ Does anyone in your group remind you of yourself? If so, why?

_____

_____

_____

Here are the nine **criminal thinking patterns**:

- victim stance
- "good person" stance
- "unique person" stance
- fear of exposure
- lack-of-time perspective
- selective effort
- use of power to control
- seek excitement first
- ownership stance

Here are the nine **addictive thinking patterns**:

- self-pity stance
- "good person" stance
- "unique person" stance
- fear of exposure
- lack-of-time perspective
- selective effort
- use of deceit to control
- seek pleasure first
- ownership stance

Criminal and Addictive Tactics

Tactics are simply behaviors that are meant to get things done. You use criminal and addictive tactics as a survival mechanism. You use them to avoid restrictions. You use them to get what you think you want. You use them to get people off your case or to avoid being held accountable for your behavior. And you also use them to avoid feeling put down or disrespected by others. Here are three types of criminal and addictive tactics, or strategies:

1. **Avoidance.** You use avoidance strategies, or tactics, to escape responsibility, to keep a low profile so you won't have to put out effort or be exposed, and to manipulate others to get what you want. For example, you might *lie by omission or commission*. This means you mislead others by telling them things that are not true. You use lies to avoid getting caught.

2. **Diversion.** You use diversion strategies, or tactics, to confuse others, to direct attention away from yourself or from the important issues, and to avoid exposure by keeping those around you distracted and focused on other things. For example, you might *point out the faults and failures of others*. You do this by talking behind people's backs and criticizing the appearance of others.

3. **Aggression.** You use aggression strategies, or tactics, to attack, intimidate, and undermine the efforts of others. You actively try to create chaos by stirring up conflict, resentment, and other hard feelings. For example, you *argue*. You do this to keep your distance from others and to get what you want.

Here are some examples of **avoidance strategies:**
- lying by omission or commission (passive and active lying)
- being deliberately vague
- staying silent to avoid notice
- playing dumb
- selective memory and attention
- minimizing (trivializing)

Here are some examples of **diversion strategies:**
- pointing out the faults of others
- magnifying (exaggerating significance)
- deliberately trying to confuse
- quibbling over words
- introducing irrelevant issues
- discussing "smokescreen" issues
- using self-shaming to avoid responsibility

Here are some examples of **aggression strategies:**
- arguing
- using threatening words or behaviors (veiled or overt)
- raging
- sarcasm and teasing
- splitting staff
- creating chaos
- attention seeking

How Do You Avoid Responsibility?

➤ What avoidance strategies, or tactics, did you use in your former life, or still use now, to get yourself off the hook?

_____

_____

➤ What diversion strategies, or tactics, did you use in your former life, or still use now, to take the focus off uncomfortable issues?

_____

_____

➤ What aggression strategies, or tactics, do you use to intimidate, threaten, or bully others, now or in your former life?

_____

_____

➤ Describe the last time you used any one of these strategies, or tactics.

_____

_____

_____

_____

➤ In group, discuss how you've used these tactics, or strategies. Write down some of the feedback you receive here.

_____

_____

_____

_____

_____

➤ Listen to the other group members describe their own tactics, or strategies. Does anyone in your group remind you of yourself? If so, why?

_____

_____

_____

_____

_____

Your New Thinking

➤ What changes have you made in your thinking since you've entered this treatment program?

EXAMPLE:

"I learned that I'll never be able to take just one drink. Not ever. I used to think I could just stay away from alcohol until I finished this program and then be able to drink socially. It's not going to happen. I've accepted that now."

_____

_____

_____

_____

_____

_____

➤ How have these changes in your thinking affected your behavior? What kinds of changes have you made in your behavior since you've entered this treatment program?

EXAMPLE:

"I no longer feel that everyone is out to get me. Because of this, I'm more trusting of others. I listen to what others say before I jump to conclusions."

_____

_____

_____

_____

_____

_____

➤ In group, discuss the changes you've made in your thinking and behavior. Then ask your peers for feedback. Write down some of their comments here.

_____

_____

_____

_____

_____

You've reviewed the basic patterns and tactics that go into criminal and addictive thinking. In part 2, you'll continue to build a foundation for your new life. You will also begin to set up your support system and set some goals.

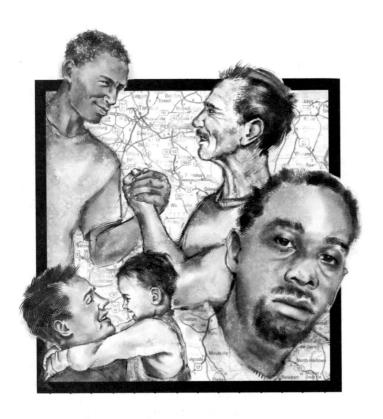

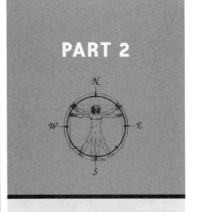
Building a Foundation for Your Future

You are now living a life that is free from alcohol, other drugs, and crime. You are moving in the right direction. Now, it's time to take the next steps that will help lay the groundwork for your success after release. In this section, you'll

- learn how to set *goals*

- identify the people and organizations you would like in your *support system*

Setting Life Goals

Setting specific, attainable, healthy goals in life is important. They will help you avoid crime and alcohol or other drug use. Whenever you set a goal, even a small one, staying sober and avoiding crime must be considered first. In this section, you will learn how to identify goals, take the steps necessary to meet those goals, and how to adapt them when necessary. Goal setting is a skill. As with other skills you have learned, you need to be flexible and identify options as you plan your life.

Why Set Goals?

Setting goals is a great way to make changes. It's true for everybody, not just ex-offenders and addicts. If you don't set goals, it's easy to drift along, not really getting anywhere. Without trying to make changes, you won't make changes. So, you can't expect any kind of life different from what you have now.

Setting Goals Helps You Leave Criminal and Addictive Thinking Behind

As a criminal and an addict, you may have lived day to day, moment to moment. Realistic goal setting wasn't a part of your life. By setting realistic goals now, you will make some important changes in your thinking. You will begin to learn how to delay gratification and face reality.

Setting Goals Helps You to Be Ambitious

Your goals should be realistic, but they should not limit you and your vision of what your life could be. Everyone has skills and experiences that are worth something in the outside world. It's time for you to identify and enhance your valuable skills. You might also need to learn some new skills. Over time, you will get a better idea of your strengths and limits. You will see where you should focus your energy and how you can direct your ambition.

"I can't just say, 'Oh, I'm going to do something healthy today.' I have to have something specific. Otherwise I get frustrated, I just drift, I get myself in trouble."

— Joe J.,
former offender,
Georgia

Having Goals Gives Your Life Purpose and Structure

Like anybody, you must consciously build a sense of purpose in life. Having goals helps you do that. You don't even have to see constant improvement. With goals, you know you have reasons for doing the work your life demands. This provides the motivation to keep going.

As your life improves, you'll be motivated even more to maintain your healthy thinking and behavior. Improvements won't happen overnight. Big things don't happen unless you make the little things happen first. The structure and routine that your goal setting brings gives you things to do. This keeps your mind occupied.

You'll Be Better Equipped to Make Healthy Decisions

Setting goals and going after them is the foundation for all the "daily life" thinking and behavior changes you'll be making. Goals help you do the following:

- be patient when things don't happen quickly

- get away from your excitement-seeking impulses

- deal with stress or frustration of any kind and not react automatically, because you don't feel trapped

- be open-minded and flexible and know you always have options

The Process of Setting Goals

Setting a goal is usually the same as setting several goals. That's because when you take a good look at a goal, it turns out that several smaller steps must be taken to achieve the main goal. Flexibility is important, too. If one of the smaller steps doesn't go quite right, it shouldn't destroy the whole process. You just make an adjustment in the one goal and keep going.

How do you move from your main goal to the supporting goals and steps? By looking at the main goal in terms of *resources*—ones you have and ones you don't have—and by looking for **obstacles** and **challenges.**

Obstacle

An *obstacle* is something that stands in the way.

Challenge

A *challenge* is something that causes a person to work harder, with more dedication.

The Nuts and Bolts of Goal Setting

Here are the five steps to goal setting:

1. Identify the goal.
2. Identify resources, obstacles, and challenges.
3. Identify new goals based on list of resources and challenges.
4. Get feedback on new goals.
5. Locate sources of support after release.

We'll use a man named Ray to help you with your goal setting. He probably has some goals that you can relate to.

STEP ONE
Identify Goal

Ray's goal: Stay clean and out of the joint for one year.

With any kind of "big" goal like this, you need to look at supporting goals first. This will include developing Ray's support network, deciding where he's going to be living, finding a job, and working on how he spends his free time. We'll first focus on Ray's job-related resources.

Identify Resources, Obstacles, and Challenges

Ray's job-related skills and resources:

- knows cars and has basic mechanical skills

- gets along well with co-workers

- has physical strength

Obstacles and challenges:

- doesn't have a job lined up

- lacks much formal work history

- not sure where to get references

- no high school diploma or formal training in mechanics

The next step involves taking a look at those resources—both the ones Ray has and the ones he needs. This is when the smaller goals come in. No matter what the size of the smaller goals, they'll all be interrelated and will be a part of the main goal of staying out of incarceration.

Step Three
Identify New Goals Based on List of Resources and Challenges

- Start looking for a first job where physical strength is necessary.

- Contact any former supervisors about references, including from jobs while incarcerated.

- Take an auto mechanics course to get formal certificate.

- Get a high school degree or GED.

Why are these good steps for Ray to take? Because they help him in his current situation and will lead to better jobs in the future. He'll need a mechanics' training certificate to be hired as a top mechanic. And having a GED opens up many employment doors.

Other goals could be added to Ray's list, but this is at least a start. No list is ever 100 percent complete and perfect. There are always choices to be made. Still, anybody—including Ray—can use help, which explains the next step.

STEP FOUR

Get Feedback on New Goals

While he is incarcerated, Ray's feedback will come mostly from his group peers. This feedback helps determine the following:

- Are his goals specific enough?

- Has Ray missed any obvious goals?

- Which are the most important goals? Which should Ray go for first?

- How will Ray know when he's reached any of these goals? What will be the measurable, specific results?

- What will Ray do if any of these goals don't work out? What are his alternatives?

Finally, while still incarcerated, Ray should also include one last step.

STEP FIVE

Locate Sources of Support for after Release

Ray simply must look for people who might be willing to help him once he's on the outside. They could be sober, responsible people he knows or organizations he could contact for help. Decisions on who to contact for support and advice on the outside should be made while incarcerated.

■

The five-step *ongoing* goal-setting process is an important concept. It must be understood before moving on further in this workbook.

Goal setting will help you plan for your housing, your job, and your free time.

Setting Up Your Support System

The first area you'll plan for your new life is your *support system.*

Besides people, your support system may also include a Twelve Step program or other recovery group, religious organizations, or government health care or job services. All of these support groups or organizations are made up of people. It's important that you communicate with these people openly and fairly. Don't look for reasons to blame them for your problems if they don't do what you want all the time.

In all these relationships with your support people, of course, you'll be practicing two very important new skills: asking for help and accepting help. This might not be something that comes naturally to you.

Everybody needs help. It's normal to ask for help *and* to receive it. We know that people who try to stay in recovery without a support system don't make it.

We'll help you find people who will be a part of your support system. Your support system may include

- a sponsor, or mentor, or more than one such person

- a few trustworthy members of your family

- a few trustworthy friends or acquaintances

You'll also be deciding whether you want to belong to two different kinds of formal organizations:

- recovery groups

- a spiritual organization of any kind

Finally, we'll be discussing your relationship with your parole officer, or supervising agent. We'll also show you how to find a counselor, should you decide you need one.

Support System

People who can help you through stressful situations are members of your *support system.* These people are trustworthy. They will help keep you away from crime and addiction.

The Characteristics of People in Your Support System

While you don't need to include a specific number of people in your support system, it's probably good to have at least five. Some people have eight or ten, with one or two or three playing the special role of sponsor, or mentor. *Any* member of your support system needs to have some basic characteristics:

- You want people who know your tactics—who can recognize the lies you tell yourself and others that lead to drinking, other drugs, or crime. "You want someone who knows your bullshit," as one ex-offender says.

- Include some people in your support network who have "been through it" and succeeded or are working real hard on it. These might be people in recovery or people who have been incarcerated. They *know* how difficult it is, and they know it's possible to succeed.

- They should *not* be exactly the same as you, in terms of their thinking patterns. Someone who is just like you has a hard time being objective.

- Support people must believe that *complete abstinence* is the only solution for addicts.

- They must be trustworthy, living their lives with responsibility, meeting their obligations to themselves and others.

- They should be experienced with the issues you'll face and able to help you find solutions to your problems.

- They must always be objective and tell you what they think, even if you don't want to hear it.

Sponsor or Mentor Characteristics

The word **sponsor** is associated with some specific recovery programs, such as Alcoholics Anonymous. The term *mentor* can also be used here. Whatever term you choose to use, at least one and probably more members of your support system must fill this special role. Sponsors or mentors must be in recovery themselves and be available to call *anytime* about *anything* that's happening in your life. They must be trustworthy, people you can tell anything to, and *specially committed to you and your recovery.* Don't choose your significant other, spouse, another relative, or someone you might be sexually attracted to. These people are too close to you and your problems.

A sponsor or mentor must have all the characteristics we've already described, and also

- be sober/clean for at least two years
- be of the same gender as you
- be active in a recovery program

Choosing People for Your Support System

Choose members of your support system carefully. Having a healthy support system is important in recovery. Without one, your chances of staying in recovery are slim.

Family members can be an important part of your support system, but only if they are living healthy, responsible lives. It's very possible that they might not want anything to do with you because of your past behavior. It will be up to you to prove to them that you really are working to change. *Friends and acquaintances* might be another option. But they must be people who are in recovery from addictive and criminal behavior. You might need to stay away from some people you were close to in your previous life.

Sponsor

A *sponsor* is a clean, sober person who is active in a recovery program. He will be the person you turn to in a crisis, the person you can call anytime. He will give you a kick in the pants when you're making excuses and offer hope when you're thinking about giving up.

"You might love your family dearly, you might plan to spend some time with them, but that doesn't mean you always want 'em as part of your support system. You've got to be honest with yourself about that."

— Roland V.,
offender,
Wisconsin

Family Members, Friends, and Acquaintances

➤ List the family members, friends, and acquaintances you respect who might be willing to be part of your support system.

_____

_____

_____

_____

_____

_____

_____

➤ In group, talk about the people you listed above. Write down some of the feedback of your peers.

_____

_____

_____

_____

_____

_____

_____

➤ Do you agree with their feedback? (check one)

_____ Yes   _____ No

Why or why not?

_____

_____

_____

➤ After discussing your choices with the group, what changes
would you like to make to this list of people?

_____

_____

_____

_____

Recovery Programs

The reasons for being in a recovery program are similar
to those for having a sponsor. You can't do this alone. The
more support you have, the better. Alcoholics Anonymous,
Narcotics Anonymous, 13 Feathers, and local recovery
organizations are all programs that offer recovery support.
These programs surround you with motivated people
you need to succeed. These programs also are where formal
sponsors or mentors are found. Let's look at your options.

5a.
What's Out There?

➤ In group, discuss any organizations that might be helpful in your recovery. List the groups available in the area where you will be living after you are released. To do this, you'll need to talk to your caseworker, therapist, and people in recovery on the outside and inside for specific information on recovery programs.

_____

_____

_____

_____

_____

■ ■ ■

5b.
Making Contacts and Exploring Options

➤ Now, use the information you gathered in 5a. to contact these groups and get answers to the following questions: When do they meet? Where do they meet? Which ones do you like, and why?

_____

_____

_____

_____

_____

_____

_____

_____

_____

_____

➤ In group, talk about the groups that you have been
exploring. Ask your peers what recovery programs you
should look into more. Write down some of the feedback
you receive.

_____

_____

_____

_____

*The reasons for
being in a recovery
program are similar
to those for having
a sponsor. You can't
do this alone.*

It's time to pull your support system together. Review-
ing exercises 4 and 5 will help you do that. Exercise 6 asks
you who you want in your support system at this time.
Remember, your support system will change and grow
as you do.

Members of Your Support Group

➤ Who are the family members, friends, and acquaintances you would like to include in your support system? You originally identified these people in exercise 4.

_____

_____

_____

_____

➤ Which recovery groups do you plan to attend once you are released? You originally identified these organizations in exercise 5.

_____

_____

_____

➤ List other people—friends, family members, or those you've met or contacted in recovery groups—who could serve as sponsors or mentors.

_____

_____

_____

Contacting Members of Your Support System

Now it's time to ask the people you listed in exercise 6 to be on your support team. Do it now. Don't wait until you are released. You are going to need these people right away. Some members of your support network will be able to help you as you prepare for release.

EXERCISE **7** EXERCISE

Contacting Your Support System

Select three family members, friends, or acquaintances that you identified in exercise 6 and answer the following questions.

➤ Members of my support team:

1. _____

2. _____

3. _____

➤ When do you plan to see each of these people?

1. _____

2. _____

3. _____

**Remember, your support system will
change and grow as you do.**

➤ How will you go about contacting each of them?

1. _____

2. _____

3. _____

EXERCISE 8 EXERCISE

Contacting Sponsors or Mentors

➤ It's especially important to contact your sponsor or mentor now, before you're released. Use the space below to write down the names and phone numbers of those who agree to fill the role. We suggest you list at least three people.

Name	Phone Number

1. _____

2. _____

3. _____

Throughout your life, members of your support group will continue to change. That's okay. In fact, it's a sign that you are growing and changing in a positive way. If members of your support group do change while working in this module, write down those changes in this workbook.

More Support

Taking care of yourself and not relapsing will help you stay out from behind bars. You also need to make sure you understand all the conditions of your parole.

> EXAMPLE:
>
> *If you have even one dirty UA, you can be placed back behind bars.*

Your Parole Officer

Your parole officer (PO), or supervising agent, will become a big part of your support system. You do not get to decide who he or she will be. Many believe that the rules of parole and probation are there just to set them up to get busted. Because of this, they have a negative attitude toward their PO. Don't do this. Instead, be respectful, honest, and trustworthy.

Probation and parole can be a positive, supportive experience. Think of it as the last leg on your journey to freedom. If you choose, you can make it work for you. It can help you manage your freedom as you try to get your life organized again. Parole officers can help you stay straight. They can be a resource for you. They know employers who hire ex-offenders. They can help you find halfway houses, community services, clothing, or emergency counseling. Work with them and ask for help when needed.

"Your PO is not your enemy. He is not out to send you back to prison. If you act like a criminal, sure—then he'll treat you like a criminal. But if you act cool, he'll work hard for you."

— Lester M.,
former offender,
Illinois

Parole Officer Specifics

➤ Once you know who your PO will be, write down the name, address, and phone number of this person.

Name:_____

Address:_____

_____

Phone number:_____

➤ Now, write down when and where your first meeting will take place and how you will get there.

Date and time of first meeting:_____

Location of first meeting:_____

Transportation: _____

Mental Health Counseling

Since you've been incarcerated, you might have discovered that you have some specific mental health issues that you need to work on. These might be anger management, sex addiction, or depression. It's important that you continue to get therapy for these issues. If you don't, you will be putting yourself at risk for relapse.

Mental Health Counseling

Complete this exercise and then ask your facilitator to review your answers to the following questions.

➤ Do you plan on meeting regularly with a counselor or therapist after you are released? (check one)

_____ Yes   _____ No

➤ Is mental health counseling a condition of your parole? (check one)

_____ Yes   _____ No

Now, think about your options for receiving regular counseling or therapy. You'll need to consider your needs, and how much you can afford to pay.

List the phone numbers and names of three clinics that are good options for you to receive counseling or therapy. (If possible, name specific therapists.)

Clinic   Phone Number

1. _____

2. _____

3. _____

> Next, either call each of these clinics yourself, or have your sponsor, mentor, or another friend do it for you. When you contact each clinic, ask the following questions:

- Are there openings?
- Is there a waiting list?
- How much will it cost?

In the space below, write the answers to the above questions.

Clinic 1:

_____

_____

Clinic 2:

_____

_____

Clinic 3:

_____

_____

> After collecting more information about your three options, which clinic is best for you?

_____

A support network may also include some kind of spiritual organization or experience.

Religion and Spirituality

A support network may also include some kind of spiritual organization or experience. This might involve attending a church, mosque, synagogue, or simply being out in nature. There are many recovering people who find such experiences to be very helpful. But only you can decide what you believe. We are not asking you to become religious or spiritual. Instead, we ask that you check out what's available and go from there.

EXERCISE **11** EXERCISE

Exploring Your Spiritual Side

In group, discuss the following questions.

➤ Are you planning on attending any spiritual groups or religious services once you're released? If so, list them here.

_____

_____

_____

➤ How often will you go to these meetings or services? How will you get there?

_____

_____

_____

➤ In group, talk about your spiritual plans, if you have any. After listening to the other group members, have you discovered any new spiritual options? List them here.

_____

_____

_____

_____

➤ If you choose not to attend an organized spiritual service, will you take time for an activity that involves silence or self-reflection? Describe your plans here.

_____

_____

_____

_____

_____

Part 3 will focus on housing options. By learning the skill of goal setting, finding someplace to live will be much easier than before.

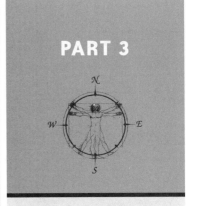

Setting Housing Goals

In part 2, you learned how to create a good support system for your new life. Use the people in your support system to help you with your next task—finding a place to live. As you will soon discover, finding a place to live will be challenging. You need a plan.

Basic Housing Issues

Remember, where you live must support your new sober and noncriminal lifestyle. Finding adequate housing will be a *major* source of stress for you. You're not alone in that, of course. Housing is expensive and can be difficult to find for everyone, not just ex-offenders. Yet you'll face some special roadblocks because of your criminal history. This will be frustrating. Therefore, you must always be *flexible,* not automatic and reactive, in your response to problems and stress.

Self-Awareness and How Others See You

Housing is one of the main areas of your life in which you'll need to deal with the perceptions of others. Because of your history of crime and addiction, you may have difficulty finding a place to live. You might also be turned down for reasons that have nothing to do with your past. There's a high demand for affordable housing. Of course, some people will judge you on your past no matter what you do. People from your old neighborhood might assume that you are unchanged once you are released. They may want to drag you back to your old lifestyle of using and crime. Don't let that affect you. You need to control *yourself.*

■

You can't control other people's actions or everything that happens to you and around you, but you can manage your feelings and control what you do.

"When I realized I had a place to go every night, someplace I knew I could sleep and just be by myself, that was a big accomplishment. That's when I really believed I could make it."

— Vernon L., halfway house resident, Minnesota

What Does "Adequate Housing" Mean?

➤ In group, discuss what it means to have a place to live that's "good enough" or "adequate." Write your answers below.

_____

_____

_____

_____

_____

Always Be Looking to Improve Your Housing Situation

At first, you may have to settle for housing that is not the greatest. Consider this transitional housing. Remind yourself that _you don't need to stay there for long._ You'll continue to set goals. You'll reach your goals by working constantly and consistently on them. This isn't something only ex-offenders must do, by the way. Everybody needs to do it. It's a gateway to a better life.

For some of you, it may at times be difficult to believe your life will get better. You may sometimes find yourself returning to the "victim" role, where you start to think you never get any breaks. You need to move past that kind of thinking now.

Your Criminal and Addictive Thinking Patterns

Think about your own thinking now. This includes your thinking patterns and tactics, which you reviewed in part 1. We will ask you to consider how that thinking has affected your housing situations during your life. You may choose to review part 1 (pages 10–18) before you complete this exercise.

EXERCISE **13** EXERCISE

Criminal and Addictive Thinking Patterns and Housing

➤ Before incarceration, how did your criminal and addictive thinking patterns affect where you lived? For example, did you live poorly because you used all your money for alcohol and other drugs?

_____

_____

_____

➤ Did your lifestyle mess up good living situations you were in? (check one)

_____ Yes   _____ No

Give a specific example.

_____

_____

_____

➤ When in your life did you have a good, healthy housing situation? What was different about your life then? For example, were you sober then? Describe that time in detail below.

_____

_____

_____

_____

_____

_____

➤ In group, discuss the topic of housing. What did you learn about your own plans for housing through this discussion?

_____

_____

_____

_____

_____

_____

Looking for Housing: The Mechanics

Now, let's spend some time thinking about how you can find housing—where to look for housing and the best ways to apply for it.

How to Look for Housing

➤ In the space below, list some places where you can find out about housing.

_____

_____

_____

➤ It's time to do some research on your own. What kind of housing will meet your short-term goals? What are the costs, and which city or neighborhood will you live in?

_____

_____

_____

➤ In group, share what you've learned about housing options. Listen to your peers do the same. Then, think about what lessons you have learned from sharing your own story and listening to other people's stories about how to find housing.

Rental Applications

➤ Fill out the sample rental application that has been provided for you.

➤ Does the application ask for any information you don't have? If so, list it here.

_____

_____

_____

_____

Your Resources, Obstacles, and Challenges

It's time to look at what resources you have available to you for your housing search. This includes your income, informal resources, and knowledge of various government housing options. We'll also look at some of the obstacles and challenges you'll face as you look for housing.

"You know what? If you want to join the rest of the world not in prison, then you have to take control of your thinking and your life."

— Ahmed A., former offender, Minnesota

Your Own Resources for Finding Housing

➤ What resources do you plan to use to find a place where you want to live after you are released?

> EXAMPLE:
>
> *Checking out the want ads to see what's available.*

_____

_____

_____

"So I'm moving in with my significant other, and she's been renting this apartment, and the landlord is going to wonder, who's this guy living there all of a sudden? Where'd he come from? And you have to tell him the deal, there's no way around it, and it can cause some trouble."

— Willie W.,
former offender,
Michigan

➤ What resources do you plan to use to find a safe place to live that will support your new sober lifestyle?

> EXAMPLE:
>
> *Going to an AA meeting and asking people if they know of any sober houses in the neighborhood you want to live in.*

_____

_____

_____

➤ What resources do you plan to use to pay for the very first place you stay in after you are released?

> EXAMPLE:
>
> *If you don't have any money, helping out in other ways like cleaning or repairing things that need to be fixed.*

_____

_____

_____

➤ What resources will you use to find a place to live in the short-term?

> EXAMPLE:
>
> *Talking with your therapist or other members of your group about housing options for people that are in recovery and are on parole.*

_____

_____

_____

➤ In group, discuss some resources for finding housing. Then, ask your peers for feedback. What resources did they mention that will save you time? Did they mention any resources that you'd like to look into? If so, write them here.

_____

_____

_____

_____

_____

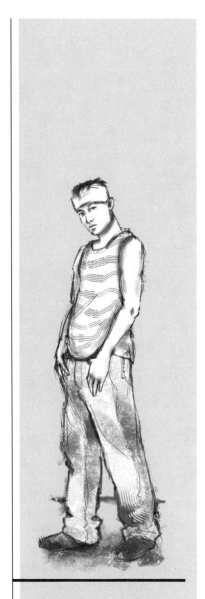

What resources do you plan to use to find a safe place to live that will support your new sober lifestyle?

Possible Obstacles and Challenges to Finding Housing

➤ What are some of your obstacles to finding housing?

_____

_____

_____

_____

➤ What are some of the challenges you may find in most places you're likely to live?

_____

_____

_____

_____

➤ In group, discuss ways you might be able to overcome or deal with these challenges. Write them down here.

_____

_____

_____

_____

"Once you really start looking—for a place to live, a job, whatever— there's more possibilities than you think. And you have more resources than you think. So you really can't be afraid to look. And you can't be looking with a bad attitude, because then you miss things."

— Paul S.,
former offender,
Wisconsin

Legal Restrictions

➤ What are your own legal restrictions that will affect where you can live? This will require some research on your own. Talk with your facilitator to learn ways to research this. If necessary, complete this exercise in a notebook.

_____

_____

_____

➤ In group, ask your peers if they have ideas on legal restrictions. Write them down here.

_____

_____

_____

➤ When you submit a rental application, the company will complete a background check on you. In group, discuss how to respond when asked about your time behind bars. Below, write down what you will say.

_____

_____

_____

_____

Goal Setting for Housing

You have already learned some basics on what you need to consider when setting and evaluating your housing goals. Now it's time to set some specific goals. Remember, housing goals may change over time.

Finding a Place to Call Home

Finding a place to live after you are released will be difficult. Here are a few options you might want to consider:

- *Sober housing* is an affordable, safe place to live while practicing the principles of recovery. It not only offers a roof over your head, but a built-in support system, too.

- *Extended care* is not inpatient drug treatment. Rather, clients receive additional therapy in an outpatient setting. They live in shared apartments, learning daily living skills for staying sober. Studies have shown that the longer a person is in drug treatment, the greater the chances for long-term sobriety.

- *Halfway house* is a term used both in the recovery and corrections world. The idea is that both ex-offenders and recovering addicts will establish community roots, find and keep a job, and follow the rules to avoid relapse. Halfway houses usually have strict guidelines for all residents, including curfews and mandatory random drug testing. These facilities are run by both nonprofit organizations and for-profit companies.

- *3/4 way house* is less strict than a halfway house. The residents have less responsibility to the operators as far as reporting, curfews, and drug testing. More personal responsibility and independence is expected from both residents and operators. Facilities may be for-profit or nonprofit.

Finding a place to live after you are released will be difficult.

- Places that provide *transitional housing* often have a very structured program for reintegrating back into society while working on staying sober.

Although these are just a few of your housing options, this list will provide you a place to start.

EXERCISE **19** EXERCISE

Your Housing Goals

➤ Where do you plan to live in the *immediate future,* the first few days after your release? Include at least one option. Why are these your choices?

_____

_____

_____

_____

➤ Where do want to live after that, in the *short term*, over the next few months or year? Include at least one option. Why are these your choices?

_____

_____

_____

_____

➤ Where would you like to live in the *long term,* after a year or two? Include at least one option.

_____

_____

_____

➤ Which people in your support system can help you as you continue to set goals for housing and deal with housing issues on the outside?

_____

_____

➤ In group, review the housing goals you've listed so far. After listening to the group feedback, are there any changes you need to make to your housing goals? If so, list your revised housing goals below.

_____

_____

_____

_____

_____

Your Plan for Housing

Now, let's turn those goals into a plan of action. View this as a series of smaller goals that get you going on the path toward your larger ones. Review the goals you listed in exercise 19. What can you do now, while still incarcerated, about your housing goals? What steps will you take after being released? Consider the following points when planning your future:

- your criminal and addictive thinking patterns

- your need to maintain sobriety

- people and situations you should stay away from

- your own housing resources: the income you expect and your informal resources

- your support network

- other resources for housing, such as temporary shelters and sober houses

- resources that seem most useful to you, including informal sources

- the obstacles you face, including your legal restrictions

- your need to be realistic, yet not "undersell" yourself

Finding a Place to Live,
What Steps to Take

It's time to turn your goals into a plan of action. Smaller goals will help get you going on the path toward your larger ones. You will need to write down specific steps you will take to find a place to live.

➤ *Steps before Release*

> EXAMPLE:
>
> *Calling family members to see if you can live with them for a short period after your release.*

_____

_____

_____

➤ *Steps after Release*

First Twenty-Four Hours:

> EXAMPLE:
>
> *Researching places where you'd like to live, such as halfway houses and sober houses. You may wish to visit these places or simply request an application.*

_____

_____

_____

First Three Days:

EXAMPLE:

Filling out housing applications.

_____

_____

_____

First Seven Days:

EXAMPLE:

Delivering those housing applications to the different housing options.

_____

_____

_____

First Few Weeks:

EXAMPLE:

Moving into a halfway house, even though it wasn't your first choice.

_____

_____

_____

Remember, your housing goals may change over time.

➤ First Six Months to a Year:

EXAMPLE:

Moving into a sober house of your choice.

_____

_____

_____

➤ In group, discuss your housing goals, both the short-term and long-term goals. Then, ask your peers for feedback about the goals you have set. List some of their comments below.

_____

_____

_____

_____

You've done it. You've set goals and planned for one of the most important areas in life: where you're going to live. This set of plans may change, so don't hesitate to write those changes down when they do occur—it's all part of being flexible. Now, let's turn to another set of important goals—where you're going to work.

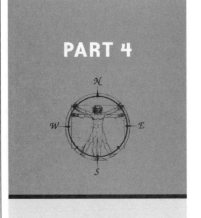

Setting Employment Goals

Where are you going to work after you are released? The exercises in this section will help you plan and set realistic goals for finding and keeping a job. You will use all the things you've learned about yourself and your thinking while participating in this program.

Basic Employment Issues

In this section, we'll explore some basic issues involving looking for work and dealing with different job situations.

Work as a Part of Your Support System

Staying sober, staying free of crime: those are the most important considerations when making decisions about where to work. *This is not an excuse not to work.* Just choose the best option you can. Wherever you end up working, deal with it responsibly and honestly.

Work is usually either a source of support or a harmful influence in your life. Think about it. The people you work with are the people you spend the most time with. If they draw you into your old thinking patterns, bad things will happen. If they understand your efforts and don't get in your way, or even help, that's incredibly valuable.

And it's not just the people. The work situation itself can be helpful or harmful, too. If you need to take a long bus ride to get to your workplace, it's probably not wise to take a job that starts at 6:30 A.M. There's no need to add more stress to your life.

Granted, you'll get frustrated and stressed out while you look for work—and in any work setting. But remember to be flexible and not respond automatically. Don't spend your time or energy judging others. Focus on becoming responsible for your own actions.

"Oh, that was a beautiful job, working maintenance at a store. The money wasn't great but I just kept doing the job, proving they could count on me. Everybody loved me. That job was what really got me going."

— Don. P.,
former offender,
Wisconsin

Identifying Helpful and Harmful Work Situations

As a group, brainstorm three examples of both helpful and harmful work situations. Then, write them below.

➤ **Helpful work situations**

EXAMPLE:

Working with co-workers who support your recovery.

1. _____

    _____

2. _____

    _____

3. _____

    _____

➤ **Harmful work situations**

EXAMPLE:

Working as a bartender when you are in recovery.

1. _____

    _____

2. _____

    _____

3. _____

Why Do We Work?

In group, discuss the following questions. Write your answers below.

➤ Why do you want to find a job?

_____

_____

_____

_____

➤ How long do you think it will take you to find a job?

_____

_____

➤ Are you willing to work at a job that might not be your first choice so you can pay the bills? Why or why not?

_____

_____

➤ How can a job help you stay sober and crime free?

_____

_____

Self-Awareness and How Others See You

Just as with housing, people may relate to you differently because you are an ex-offender looking for work. Even after you've been hired for a job, you will be viewed differently because of your criminal record. That's the reality of the situation. It's important to keep reminding yourself that you can't control the actions or beliefs of others. You can, however, manage your own reactions and emotions, react flexibly, and control what you do.

You don't have to react negatively when someone presents an obstacle, like not hiring you. *You're not entitled to any job.* It's another person's decision, and it should not have any effect on your own behavior. Being turned down may have nothing to do with your criminal history. It happens to everybody. It's normal to be turned down. Sometimes, you may want to ask why you didn't get a particular job that you applied for. It doesn't hurt to ask. It may give you a little information for next time, even if the reason is your criminal record. The employer may be impressed with your initiative and remember you if he or she is ever hiring again.

EXERCISE 23 EXERCISE

What Is an "Adequate" Job?

➤ What do you think is an adequate job for you when you are released? In group, read your answer out loud.

_____

_____

_____

Your Criminal and Addictive Thinking Patterns

Now, think about your own thinking. This includes your thinking patterns and tactics, which you reviewed in part 1. We will ask you to consider how that thinking has affected your employment experiences. You may choose to review part 1 (pages 10–16) before you complete this exercise.

EXERCISE **24** EXERCISE

Criminal and Addictive Thinking Patterns and Employment

➤ Before incarceration, how did your criminal and addictive thinking patterns and behaviors affect your job situations? How did they affect where you worked, if you worked, or how you got along with people at work?

_____

_____

_____

_____

_____

➤ Give an example of a situation from one of your past jobs where you used your criminal and addictive thinking.

_____

_____

_____

➤ When in your life did you have a good, healthy employment situation? What was different about your life then? For example, were you sober then? Describe that time below.

_____

_____

_____

_____

➤ In group, discuss some of the skills you've developed through the jobs you have had in life so far. Then, ask your peers for feedback. After listening to their feedback, what additions could you make to your list?

_____

_____

_____

_____

➤ What lessons have you learned from sharing your own story and listening to other people's stories about employment?

_____

_____

_____

Your Resources, Obstacles, and Challenges

In this section, we'll look at the resources you have available for your job search. We'll also consider the kinds of obstacles or special challenges you might face as an ex-offender seeking employment.

Your Job Situation and Resources

➤ Do you have your first job lined up for after you are released? (check one)

_____ Yes _____ No

If so, what is it?

_____

_____

➤ Do you have a backup job in case this doesn't work out? (check one)

_____ Yes _____ No

➤ What is your level of education? For example, did you graduate from high school or community college, or do you have other special training?

_____

_____

_____

_____

What are some of the skills you've developed through the jobs you have had in life so far?

➤ What educational resources are available to you now, while you're incarcerated? How might they be helpful to you?

_____

_____

_____

_____

➤ List your work history. Where have you worked and for how long? Include jobs you've had while incarcerated.

_____

_____

_____

_____

_____

_____

_____

_____

_____

"I said, job skills? I know how to rob somebody, do a physical assault, but other than that . . . The thing is, though, everybody's got enough job skills to get the first job. And after that, if you do it right, you're in."

— Lenny F.,
former offender,
Minnesota

➤ What types of useful experience did you gain from these jobs?

_____

_____

_____

_____

➤ What other kinds of resources and skills do you have that will help you find work? These might include physical strength, being a quick learner, or other life experiences. Think broadly.

_____

_____

_____

_____

➤ In group or with your therapist, describe all your resources and then ask for feedback. Do you agree with their comments? Why or why not? After listening to their feedback, do you have any additions you would like to make to your list? If so, write them here.

_____

_____

_____

Possible Obstacles and Challenges
in Finding Employment

➤ What are your own legal restrictions that will affect where you can work?

_____

_____

_____

_____

➤ How will you respond, in an interview or in a job application, when asked about your criminal history?

_____

_____

_____

_____

➤ Describe other potential obstacles you see to getting a job and how you can deal with these challenges.

_____

_____

_____

_____

➤ In group or with your therapist, describe these obstacles and your plans for dealing with them. Write their feedback here.

_____

_____

_____

_____

_____

■

How and Where to Look for Work

Next, we'll explore some of the basic steps you'll need to take as you enter the job market. The following exercises will cover how and where to look for jobs, how to write a résumé and fill out an application, and how to skillfully handle a job interview.

"There's always jobs out there. They're like deer in the woods next to the highway. The more you look, the more you find."

— Kevin B.,
halfway house resident,
Nebraska

How and Where to Look for Work

➤ In group, brainstorm a list of places where you could look for work. Write the list here.

_____

_____

_____

_____

_____

➤ Review the list of job ideas. Which jobs from the list interest you the most?

> EXAMPLE:
>
> _Being a lawyer._

_____

_____

_____

➤ Why does this job most interest you?

> EXAMPLE:
>
> _This is a job where I can make a lot of money._

_____

_____

_____

➤ In group, discuss what job interests you the most. After listening to all the group members, what other job do you want to learn more about?

EXAMPLE:

Being a mechanic.

_____

_____

➤ How will you go about doing this?

EXAMPLE:

After I'm released, I'll go to the local technical college to see how long it takes to become a mechanic. Then, I'll see if I can get a job in an autoshop to see if I like working in that type of environment.

_____

_____

_____

_____

_____

_____

_____

What job interests you the most? What other job do you want to learn more about?

Writing a Résumé

A **résumé** is a brief description of your skills and work history. There are two types:

- A résumé that lists your work history, starting with the most recent. This is called a *chronological résumé.*

- A résumé that concentrates on your skills. This type may work best for you if you don't have a long work history. This is called a *functional résumé.*

It's always a good idea to have a résumé, *even when you have a job.* In fact, the minute you get a new job, your résumé should be updated. This isn't something you do once and then forget about. The fact is, no job lasts forever. You *will* need a résumé again at some point. Update it on a regular basis.

 EXERCISE 28 EXERCISE

Writing a Résumé

➤ In your notebook or on a computer or typewriter, write your own résumé.

➤ Next, pair off with another member of your group and review each other's résumés. Write down any feedback you receive and make appropriate changes directly on your résumé.

EXERCISE 29 EXERCISE

Job Applications

➤ Fill out the sample job application form that has been provided for you.

➤ If there is a question about your criminal history on the job application, how will you respond?

_____

_____

_____

_____

EXERCISE 30 EXERCISE

Job Interviews

➤ In group, brainstorm some things you need to keep in mind while preparing for an interview. Write the list here.

_____

_____

_____

_____

_____

➤ It's time to do a practice interview for a job you would consider applying for in real life. After the interview, the facilitator will give you some feedback on how you did. Write down some of that feedback here. What did you do well? Did you learn any ways you could improve your interviewing skills? What are some things you need to be aware of while interviewing?

_____

_____

_____

_____

_____

_____

_____

_____

"One thing I've learned is, if you show up the second week, you're already way ahead of a lot of jerks out there."

— Wally S., former offender, Minnesota

How to Keep a Job

Getting a job is only the first step, of course. You also need to handle a job well, in all kinds of ways. In this section, we'll discuss some of the requirements you need to meet to hang on to any job.

EXERCISE **31** EXERCISE

Keeping a Job

➤ In group, brainstorm some basic requirements for keeping a job. Write the list here.

_____

_____

_____

_____

_____

_____

_____

_____

_____

Getting to Work on Time: Transportation

➤ Your assignment is to find out how to get information about transportation schedules. This might be for the bus, subway, or whatever form of public transportation exists where you are going to be living. List the information sources you intend to use below. You might also research how long it takes to get from one point to another. Write what you learn here.

_____

_____

_____

_____

_____

_____

_____

_____

_____

_____

_____

How to Advance in Your Job

As we've stated throughout this workbook, it's important for you to be realistic *but ambitious* in your new life. A job is a good place to start being ambitious. Think in terms of small steps. Be flexible, too. There are a lot of ways to be ambitious and to advance. They don't all have to involve big promotions or raises in pay. For example, after a period of doing your job well, you may ask for additional responsibilities.

EXERCISE **33** EXERCISE

Ambition on the Job

➤ List potential places where you may be able to find a job right after you are released or soon thereafter. What paths are there for moving up in this company?

_____

_____

_____

_____

➤ In group, ask your peers to evaluate what you've written and provide you some feedback. What are their thoughts on being promoted? Do they know of people who have moved up in their jobs because of their work ethic?

_____

_____

_____

"Once you're in, you can always move up. You can always climb the ladder. Don't worry about reaching the end of the ladder— just worry about the next rung."

— Ron H.,
former offender,
Connecticut

Thinking Long Term

➤ Are you considering moving into a line of work that is completely different from what you've done in the past? (check one)

_____ Yes   _____ No

If so, what are some of the options you'd like to consider? Don't worry if an option doesn't seem realistic. It's okay to dream about a better future and work toward that. Write down some options here.

_____

_____

_____

_____

_____

➤ Is there a job you could try for first? Maybe it's something that would move you in the direction you want to go. List at least two possibilities.

_____

_____

_____

_____

It's important for you to be realistic but ambitious in your new life.

➤ List any steps you could take to advance, including education options.

_____

_____

_____

_____

_____

_____

➤ In group, discuss your ideas for advancing in a job or getting a better job. Then, ask your peers and facilitator for feedback. Write their comments here.

_____

_____

_____

_____

_____

_____

Goal Setting for Employment

We've covered some basics on what you need to consider when setting your employment goals and making your plans for release. Now it's time for some specific goal setting.

Your Employment Goals

➤ After you're released, where would you like to work in the short term, for the first few weeks or months? Include at least two backup options.

_____

_____

_____

_____

_____

➤ In the longer term, after a year or two or three, where would you like to be working? Include at least one option.

_____

_____

_____

_____

_____

➤ In group, discuss your employment goals. Then, ask your peers for feedback. Do you agree with their comments? (check one)

_____ Yes   _____ No

➤ After hearing their feedback, would you like to make any changes to your employment goals? Write them down here.

_____

_____

_____

_____

_____

_____

_____

_____

"This friend of mine, he just decided he didn't want people running his life anymore. So he got a job, and now he runs his own business, and he did it, man. It's possible. You can do it."

— Kevin B., halfway house resident, Nebraska

Finding a Job, What Steps to Take

It's time to turn your goals into a plan of action. Smaller goals will help get you going on the path toward your larger ones. You will need to write down specific steps you will take to find a place to work.

➤ *Steps before Release*

EXAMPLE:

Asking your facilitator and peers if they know of places that are willing to hire ex-offenders.

_____

_____

_____

_____

➤ *Steps after Release*

First Twenty-Four Hours:

EXAMPLE:

Writing down the names, addresses, and phone numbers of some of the potential employers you identified while you were still incarcerated.

_____

_____

_____

What kinds of resources and skills do you have that will help you find work?

First Three Days:

> EXAMPLE:
>
> *Calling those potential employers or dropping by to fill out a job application.*

First Seven Days:

> EXAMPLE:
>
> *Completing the job applications.*

First Few Weeks:

> EXAMPLE:
>
> *Setting up interviews with potential employers.*

First Six Months to a Year:

EXAMPLE:

Earning enough money to pay your bills.

_____

_____

Long Term—after a Year or Two:

EXAMPLE:

Earning enough money to pay your bills,
plus have a savings account.

_____

_____

In group, discuss your employment goals, both your short-term and long-term goals. Then, ask your peers for feedback about the goals you have set. List some of their comments below.

_____

_____

_____

You've now planned for your housing and your job search. This is a great foundation that you can build upon throughout your life. Now you'll learn how to live on a budget and use your free time wisely.

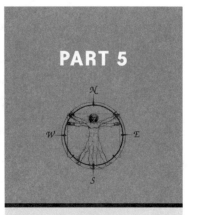

Your Budget and Free Time

Your decisions about spending money are critical to your recovery. Learning how to handle your money well and to live on a budget will be incredibly helpful as your begin your new life. Closely related to your money decisions are the choices you'll make about spending your free time. These decisions are more important than you think.

Your Budget

In the first part of this section, you'll:

- develop a basic budget for after you get a job

- develop a budget for the first week after your release

Your first priority in handling money is to do it in a way that supports a sober and noncriminal lifestyle. *Don't spend money you don't have. Delay gratification.* Take care of your most important needs first.

Your Income and Expenses

It's time to consider what your money situation will look like on the outside. This means estimating what your income will be once you get a job and identifying potential sources of income in the short term, before you have a job. Then, you'll create a basic budget for your new life.

EXERCISE **37** EXERCISE

Your Expected Income from Employment

➤ In reality, how much money do you expect to be taking home once you find your first job? This is called your "take-home" pay. This pay will be about two-thirds of your total wages.

_____

_____

Your Immediate Short-Term Income

After your release, some of you will not be starting a job for a while. Even if you are, you probably won't be paid right away, but you'll still need money right away.

EXERCISE 38 EXERCISE

Sources of Income

➤ What will be your sources of income immediately after your release? How much money will you be able to expect from those sources? Because this exercise will take some research on your part, you may choose to use your support network to help you out.

Sources of Income   Expected Income

_____   _____

_____   _____

_____   _____

_____   _____

_____   _____

_____   _____

_____   _____

_____   _____

➤ What steps do you need to take to pursue these sources of income, either while still incarcerated or after your release?

_____

_____

_____

_____

_____

➤ In group, discuss where you plan to get money immediately after you are released. Then, ask your peers for feedback. Write some of their comments below.

_____

_____

_____

_____

_____

_____

_____

_____

Your Expenses

Now, do some research and thinking on the basic living expenses you'll face upon your release. For your estimated housing expenses, refer to part 3 of this workbook. Talk to support people on the outside about the costs of basic living. Also talk to more experienced peers in the group. You may want to provide a range of costs for some of these expenses since it may not be possible to learn the exact cost. You will need to do this work on your own and then get feedback from the group.

EXERCISE **39** EXERCISE

Your Basic Budget

➤ *Fixed Monthly Expenses*

For each of these items, fill in an estimated *monthly* amount. (Note: Not all these expenses will apply to you.)

Rent . . . . $ _____

Phone service . . . . $ _____

Other utilities. . . . . $ _____

Transportation (car payments, gas,
bus or subway fares) . . . . $ _____

Insurance (health, life, etc.). . . . . $ _____

Child care, including support payments . . . . . $ _____

Debt repayments (loans, credit cards) . . . . $ _____

Other _____ $ _____

Other _____ $ _____

Total Fixed Monthly Expenses $ _____

➤ *Flexible Monthly Expenses*

For each of these items, fill in an estimated *monthly* amount.

Groceries .... $ _____

Clothing and shoes .... $ _____

Eating out (restaurants) .... $ _____

Magazines, newspapers, CDs, etc............. $ _____

Leisure-time activities (movies, etc.)......... $ _____

Cell phone bills .... $ _____

Savings .... $ _____

Other small expenses
(toothpaste, other toiletries, etc.)............ $ _____

Other _____ $ _____

Total Flexible Monthly Expenses $ _____

➤ *Periodic Expenses*

For each of these items, fill in an estimated *yearly* amount.

Car expenses (insurance, tab and
plate renewal, maintenance and repairs) ... $ _____

Emergencies .... $ _____

Home maintenance and repair .... $ _____

Health expenses not covered by insurance
(prescription medications, over-the counter
medicines, counseling, clinic visits) .... $ _____

Dental work................................... $ _____

Other _____ $ _____

Total Periodic Expenses $ _____

➤ In group, brainstorm ways to lower any of these expenses when you need to. Write the list of ideas here.

EXAMPLE:

Buying a calling card instead of having a long-distance phone service.

_____

_____

_____

_____

_____

_____

_____

_____

_____

"I always just used to pretend I had enough money. That always got me by, up until I went to prison, anyway."

— Randy T., former offender, California

What to Do When You Don't Have Enough Money

There may well be times when you simply do not have enough money to pay your monthly bills. It happens to most of us. And it's not the end of the world.

EXERCISE **40** EXERCISE

Not Having Enough Money to Pay the Bills

➤ In group, brainstorm ideas about what you can do when you don't have enough money to pay the bills. Write the list of ideas here.

_____

_____

_____

_____

_____

_____

_____

_____

_____

The First Seven Days after Release

In this section, you will itemize your daily costs from day one to day seven after your release. The idea here is not to write down your fixed expenses like rent, insurance, and utilities. Instead, you will work on figuring out what you want to do those first seven days after your release and what each activity will cost.

It's important to realize that many activities will cost you money. And if you don't have much money, you'll need to make some choices. For example, you might want to go out for lunch and dinner on day one, but there's a cost attached to doing so. It's important to realize that and make careful choices. After looking at how much eating out will cost you, you may decide to go out to a fast-food restaurant for lunch and then prepare your own meal for dinner.

EXERCISE **41** EXERCISE

Expenses Immediately after Release

➤ On the expense sheet on page 97, list activities and expenses you expect to have during the first seven days after your release. Do not include your fixed monthly expenses. Instead, just write down costs associated with activities you plan to do during the first seven days. For example, where do you plan to eat these first seven days? Also, think about activities you might be interested in doing. Do you want to go to a movie? Will you want soda and popcorn, too?

When you have finished writing down your anticipated expenses for these seven days, add up the daily costs and write that down, too.

Are your expenses higher than expected?

It's important to realize that many activities will cost you money. You'll need to make some choices.

If you don't have enough money to pay for all of the activities you would like to do during your first seven days after your release, then you'll need to cut something out or choose a lower-cost alternative. It's important to realize that you have choices.

➤ Below, write down any activities that cost little or no money that you could substitute for any costly activities you've written down. For example, instead of going to that movie in the movie theater, you may choose to rent a movie or go for a walk.

_____

_____

_____

_____

➤ Where do you plan to get the money to live off of during this first week?

_____

➤ In group, ask your peers for feedback about activities that are free or low cost. Write some of their comments below.

_____

_____

_____

MY SEVEN-DAY EXPENSE SHEET

	ACTIVITY	COST
DAY 1 TOTAL DAY'S EXPENSES BELOW $ _____		
DAY 2 TOTAL DAY'S EXPENSES BELOW $ _____		
DAY 3 TOTAL DAY'S EXPENSES BELOW $ _____		
DAY 4 TOTAL DAY'S EXPENSES BELOW $ _____		
DAY 5 TOTAL DAY'S EXPENSES BELOW $ _____		
DAY 6 TOTAL DAY'S EXPENSES BELOW $ _____		
DAY 7 TOTAL DAY'S EXPENSES BELOW $ _____		
	TOTAL EXPENSES FOR SEVEN DAYS	$

You've now made plans regarding your housing, finding a job, and creating a basic budget. These are three very important areas of your new life. Now, we'll move on to something that might be fun—how you are going to spend your free time after you are released.

Free Time and Leisure Activities

Your decisions about free time are critical to your recovery. Any *unstructured* time can lead to great opportunities, if you find something healthy and challenging to do. But it can also lead to danger, especially if you have *nothing* to do. Your task is to find new ways to have fun, replacing that old need for "excitement at all costs."

Relationships and Sex

Choose the people you hang out with carefully. Avoid getting into a romantic relationship with someone who abuses alcohol or other drugs. Besides tempting you to use, it's a whole lifestyle issue. Someone who abuses alcohol and other drugs has a lifestyle that is irresponsible, dishonest, and will lead back into criminal activity, too. Criminal and addictive behavior go hand in hand.

Relapsing to Manipulation

Controlling others for your own ends or treating them as objects so you can satisfy your wants is no longer an option. Entering into a sexual relationship shortly after your release can easily lead you back into your old controlling ways. Just be aware of this. Don't throw yourself into a relationship right away. If you are already in a committed relationship, then it becomes a chance for you to practice being the "new you."

Your Own Criminal and Addictive Thinking Patterns

In your former life, your free time often sent you off in the wrong direction. This is another example of how your criminal and addictive thinking patterns affected yet another area of your life.

 EXERCISE 42 EXERCISE

Criminal and Addictive Thinking Patterns and Free Time

➤ While living in your old lifestyle, how were your criminal and addictive thinking patterns and behaviors related to how you spent your free time? Write some examples below.

EXAMPLE:

You might have thought that nothing ever works out for you, so you deserved to get high.

_____

_____

_____

Choose the people you hang out with carefully.

➤ In group, discuss your examples and ask your peers for feedback. What lessons can you draw from this event about your criminal and addictive thinking patterns and behaviors?

_____

_____

_____

Healthy Excitement Seeking

➤ In group, brainstorm some inexpensive, healthy, noncriminal ways to have fun and experience excitement. Write the list of ideas here.

_____

_____

_____

_____

_____

Your Resources, Obstacles, and Challenges

➤ What healthy activities would you like to explore in your free time?

_____

_____

_____

_____

_____

➤ What are your resources for getting involved in these activities?

_____

_____

_____

➤ What are your obstacles, including costs, and how might you deal with these challenges?

_____

_____

_____

➤ In group, discuss the ideas you have for free-time activities. Then, ask your peers for feedback. Write some of their comments here.

_____

_____

_____

_____

Pursuing Romantic Relationships

➤ Do you have any legal restrictions keeping you from seeking sexual relationships after you are released? (check one)

_____ Yes   _____ No

If so, list those legal restrictions here.

_____

_____

➤ Are you now in a relationship? (check one)

_____ Yes   _____ No

If so, describe any risk factors you see in terms of criminal and addictive thinking patterns.

_____

_____

➤ In group, discuss the topic of romantic relationships. What have you learned through this discussion?

_____

_____

_____

Avoid getting into a romantic relationship with someone who abuses alcohol or other drugs.

Dangers of Seeking
Sexual Relationships Too Soon

➤ In group, brainstorm the dangers you may face in seeking out sexual relationships in the first days and weeks after you are released. Write the list of ideas here.

_____

_____

_____

_____

_____

_____

Goal Setting:
Free Time and Leisure Activities

➤ In the short term, what are some of your goals for fun and relaxation when you are released?

_____

_____

_____

_____

➤ Who will be your friends in the short term? Include a few possible names.

_____

_____

_____

_____

➤ How do you plan to deal with your old friends once you are released? How do your plan to form new, healthy friendships?

_____

_____

_____

_____

➤ In group, discuss the topic of friendships. What have you learned about your own relationships through this discussion?

_____

_____

_____

_____

Your Plan:
Free Time and Leisure Activities

➤ What steps will you take to set up these activities *before you are released?*

> EXAMPLE:
>
> *"I will ask my son if he wants to play basketball with me at the YMCA twice a week."*

_____

_____

➤ What steps will you take *the day you are released?*

> EXAMPLE:
>
> *"I will get a membership at the YMCA and check out the available court times."*

_____

_____

➤ What steps will you take *the first week?*

> EXAMPLE:
>
> *"I will ask my son if he is available to play on those days."*

_____

_____

➤ After that, what will you do regularly?

EXAMPLE:

"Since I want to play basketball as often as I can, I'll see if my son and I can join a team that plays regularly. Even if my son can't commit to playing this often, I will sign myself up. That way, I'll be sure to play often."

_____

_____

➤ In group, discuss the topic of free time and how your peers plan to deal with this. List any new ideas that come out of that discussion that you'd like to try.

_____

_____

_____

_____

_____

That's it, the last major area of your life you're going to plan. You've covered an awful lot of ground, haven't you? Housing, jobs, money, free time—you should be proud that you've worked to lay such a solid foundation for yourself. In the final part of this workbook, you'll be asked to write all this information down in one place. And this will be your release and reintegration plan.

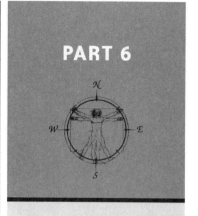

Your Plan for Life after Release

You're done. You've got your goals, budgets, and plans all written down in this workbook. In this final section, you are going to review the work you've done and write down your complete plan for the first day and the first week you are out, on the worksheets provided.

The First Day

➤ *Getting Going*

Who will pick you up from the correctional institution you are now in?

_____

Where will you go first, when you're released?

_____

_____

➤ *Support System*

Do you have a sobriety group meeting to attend on the first day? (check one)

_____ Yes   _____ No

If so, where is the meeting? How will you get there?

_____

_____

_____

Do you have a meeting with your parole officer the first day? (check one)

_____ Yes   _____ No

If so, where is the meeting? How will you get there?

_____

_____

_____

What other steps will you take to contact your support people the first day out?

_____

_____

_____

_____

➤ *Housing*

Where are you going to sleep the first night? How will you get there?

_____

_____

What specific steps will you take to arrange for more permanent housing?

_____

_____

_____

➤ *Employment*

What specific steps will you take on the first day for arranging a job?

_____

_____

_____

_____

➤ *Budget and Money*

What will your expenses be the first day out?

_____

_____

_____

How do you intend to pay for these expenses?

_____

_____

➤ *Free Time and Leisure Activities*

What will you do for fun on the first day?

_____

_____

What specific steps will you take on the first day for arranging a job?

_____

_____

■ ■ ■

In group, discuss what you'll do on your first day after you are released. Then, ask your peers for feedback. List any changes or additions you'd like to make to your plan after receiving this feedback.

_____

_____

_____

 **EXERCISE 50 EXERCISE**

The First Week

➤ *Support System*

Do you have a sobriety group meeting to attend the first week? (check one)

_____ Yes   _____ No

If so, how many and where? How will you get there?

_____

_____

Do you have a meeting with your parole officer the first week? (check one)

_____ Yes _____ No

If so, where is the meeting? How will you get there?

_____

_____

What other steps will you take to contact your support people during the first week?

_____

_____

_____

➤ *Housing*

Where are you going to sleep the first week?

_____

_____

What specific steps will you take to arrange for longer-term housing?

_____

_____

_____

➤ *Employment*

Do you have a job to go to the first week? (check one)

_____ Yes   _____ No

If yes, where is it located? How will you get there?

_____

_____

_____

If no, what specific steps will you take to find a job the first week out?

_____

_____

_____

_____

➤ *Budget and Money*

What will your expenses be the first week?

_____

_____

_____

_____

When you take care of your body, mind, and spirit, you create a positive balance that supports your recovery.

How will you pay for these items?

_____

_____

➤ *Free Time and Leisure Activities*

If you have time, what will you do for fun the first week?

_____

_____

_____

_____

■ ■ ■

➤ In group, discuss your plans for your first week after release. Then ask your peers for feedback. List any changes or additions you would like to make to your plan after receiving this feedback.

_____

_____

_____

_____

Conclusion

You're about to be released. Here are some important points to remember as you begin your new life:

- Your recovery is your number one priority. Every decision you make, every action you take, must support your need to keep away from alcohol and other drugs and to stay free of crime.

- Keep flexible. Always realize you have options. Be flexible in how you react to situations.

- Have goals—realistic, specific goals. Even though your goals must be realistic, don't be afraid to be ambitious, either. Over time, you can make a lot of progress.

- Stress and frustration will happen. That doesn't mean you're doing something wrong. It happens to everybody.

And that leads into a final thought we'd like to leave you with. It's good to start each day with a schedule. Follow it as closely as you can. But don't let this schedule be too rigid. If you aren't able to follow the schedule exactly as planned, that's okay. Build in some flexibility. When setting a schedule, try not to plan several important events all in a row. For example, what if your bus is late? What if you have to wait thirty minutes at your parole officer's office—meaning you miss your first computer class?

Attitude is also important.

When something goes wrong, the effect is never as bad as you might fear. Remember, there are always options. Job interviews can be rescheduled. There are ways to cover missed class material. Relax. Take it in stride. If you're always on edge, convinced that one mistake will become a crisis, you won't make it.

Congratulations! By doing the work in this workbook, you've accomplished something big. Take this workbook with you once you are released. It's your map for your new life as a crime-free, drug-free person. By following the plan in this workbook, your chances of recovery are much better.

You've got a chance to go at life from a whole new angle. You've prepared yourself. You've put in the work that shows you're committed to success. Once you're released, if you put in the same effort, one day others will see you and say, "There's a guy who made it. He proves it's possible."

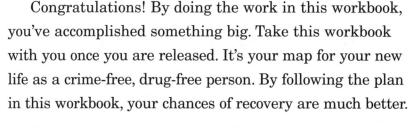

*"One of the hardest things
I learned was not to panic.
I come out with all these plans,
all these schedules, and I
needed to learn—hey! It's not
all gonna go like clockwork.
Some days it does.
Some days it doesn't."*

— Lawrence L., Halfway house resident, Michigan

NOTES

NOTES

NOTES